MALE & FEMALE

created He them

Male & Female Created He Them
Art Direction & Writing: Jordon P. Frye
© Jordon P. Frye 2023
An imprint of Truth Book Co., LLC
Anderson, IN
Printed in the United States of America
ISBN: 979-8-9862147-4-0, hardcover
ISBN: 979-8-9862147-2-6, paperback
ISBN: 979-8-9862147-3-3, ebook

For information about special discounts, bulk purchases, or
hosting a live event, please contact truthbookco@gmail.com.

MALE & FEMALE

created He them

by Jordon P. Frye

for my son,
Jamison Parker Frye

So God created man in his own image, in the image of God created he him; male and female created he them.

– Genesis 1:27

In the start, there was but dark.
But when God spoke, there was a spark.

God made everything that we can see.
The earth, the sky, the sea,
all the creatures that could be.

He made the bees, a he and a she,
buzzing about from tree to tree.

He made the lions, both loud and free,
a strong he and a gentle she.

Look above, what do we see?
Birds in the sky, both he and she.

Look below, in the deep blue sea,
two fish swimming, both he and she.

In the meadow where the grass is green, graze the cows both he and she.

All the animals had a mate,
but none of them yet had a name.
So God formed man from the earth,
and watched as he got to work.

Man named each animal,
from big to small.
From the towering giraffes,
to the ants that crawl.

Yet in this grand task he felt all alone,
for he had no "she" to call his own.

In deep sleep God placed the man,
from his rib formed a perfect plan.
When he woke the man would see,
God had made for him a she.

Man opened his eyes and saw her there,
graceful and meek beyond compare.
With a gentle spirit and tender heart,
she truly was a work of art.

All was how God meant it to be,
He made the man and then made a she.
From this plan all life would stem,
that's why male and female created He them.

Milton Keynes UK
Ingram Content Group UK Ltd.
UKRC030148120124
435900UK00007B/57